How to Write a Paragraph

Grades 5-10

Written by T.R. Gadd, B.A., M.Ed.
Illustrated by S&S Learning Materials

ISBN 1-55035-532-5
Copyright 1997
Revised January 2006
All Rights Reserved * Printed in Canada

Published in the United States by:
On the Mark Press
3909 Witmer Road PMB 175
Niagara Falls, New York
14305
www.onthemarkpress.com

Published in Canada by:
S&S Learning Materials
15 Dairy Avenue
Napanee, Ontario
K7R 1M4
www.sslearning.com

Look For Other Language Units

Reading Response Forms .... Gr. 1-3
Reading Response Forms 4-6
The First 100 Sight Words:
    Multisensory Worksheets 1
Sight Word Activities 1
Creativity With Food 4-8
What's the Scoop on Words 4-6
Poetry & Creative Writing 4-6
Personal Spelling Dictionary 2-5
Building Word Families #1 (Short Vowels) 1-2
Passport to Adventure 7-8
Building Word Families #2 (Long Vowels) 2-3
How to Write an Essay 7-12
How to Write a Paragraph 5-10
How to Write a Composition 6-10
Passion of Jesus: Play 7-9
ESL Teaching Ideas K-8
Multi-Level Spelling Program 3-6
Spelling 1
Spelling 2
Spelling 3
Spelling 4
Spelling 5
Spelling 6
Exercises in Grammar 6
Exercises in Grammar 7
Exercises in Grammar 8
Spelling Blacklines 1
How to Give a Presentation 4-6
Fun With Phonics 1-3
Literature Response Forms 1-3
Literature Response Forms 4-6
Teacher's Guide to the Grade 6 Language Test 6
Teacher's Guide to the Grade 3 Test 3

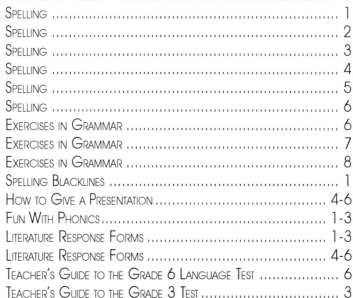

Table of Contents

What is a Paragraph? 4

Exercises in Unity? 5

Exercises in Topic Sentence 9

Coherence 22

Exercises in Coherence 25

Exercises in Concluding Sentence 31

Types of Paragraphs 34

     Exposition, Narration, Description

Using the Writing Process 45

     Prewriting, Writing the First Draft, Editing and Revising,

     Writing the final copy

Aims of the Unit

This resource is designed as a companion piece to *How to Write an Essay* and *How to Write a Composition*. Its aim is to help students write various kinds of paragraphs from grades five through the first years of secondary school. It will be helpful for students at higher levels of education who have had difficulty with writing in earlier years.

The resource contains many work sheets which can be used individually by students or in groups. Many of these work sheets are most useful if completed by pairs of students. It is also advisable for students to discuss the ideas generated by the work sheets in larger groups.

Much of this resource is written from a student perspective, so that teachers may give students the pages which they need or so that students can purchase the resource to use as they write their compositions at home.

WHAT IS A PARAGRAPH?

A paragraph is a group of sentences which all talk about one topic or subject or idea. Sometimes a paragraph can stand alone. In this case, all the sentences will talk about only one thing. If a paragraph contains sentences which all discuss one idea, the paragraph is said to possess **UNITY**. Unity means that there is only one idea in the paragraph. The sentences in the paragraph do not talk about any other ideas, only the main idea.

The main idea of the paragraph is stated in the **TOPIC SENTENCE**. The topic sentence is usually the first sentence in the paragraph, but it does not have to be. Sometimes the topic sentence may be in the second, third, fourth or even the last sentence in a paragraph. A writer who pays attention to the topic sentence and writes a good one will ensure that the paragraph possesses unity. The **CONCLUDING SENTENCE** is not only the last sentence in the paragraph, but it has another job: It sums up the main idea of the paragraph.

But the sentences in the paragraph also have to be arranged in order that makes some sense. This arrangement of sentences is called **COHERENCE**. If a paragraph possesses coherence, then one sentence will lead logically to another. The writer will not skip around or jump from one idea to another. There are many different ways to create coherence in a paragraph and some of these are discussed in the next few pages.

A good paragraph is one which contains unity and coherence. The ideas are presented in the topic sentence and summed up in the concluding sentence.

Usually, a paragraph does not stand alone. It is part of a longer piece of writing which consists of several (or sometimes many) paragraphs. The connected paragraph is discussed in a later section of this resource.

EXERCISES IN UNITY

A) The topic sentence for a paragraph is given below, followed by a number of details. Decide which details should be included in a paragraph which uses the topic sentence. Cross out details which should not be included. Give a reason why you have chosen to discard each detail.

TOPIC SENTENCE: **Sam is one of the best players on the baseball team.**

DETAILS:

1. Sam is a good athlete.

2. Sam is very tall for his age.

3. Sam likes to eat pizza, but he does not like spaghetti.

4. Sam hit two home runs in the last game.

5. Baseball is one of the best games played professionally in North America.

6. When the pitcher throws the ball, Sam has a good eye and can determine where the ball will go in relation to the plate.

7. Sam can run to first base faster than anyone on the team.

8. Sam is a member of the safety patrol at school.

9. Baseball was invented by Abner Doubleday in Cooperstown, New York.

10. Sam can pitch, hit and catch very well.

11. Sam is a very good player at first base or short stop.

12. Michelle is almost as good a player as Sam.

13. Sam likes the new glove his father bought him for his birthday.

14. Sam can read the pitcher very well and knows when he should attempt to steal a base.

15. One day when our team was losing, Sam hit a grand-slam home run, which allowed us to win the game.

16. Sam prefers baseball to hockey.

EXERCISES IN UNITY (Continued)

B) The topic sentence for a paragraph is given below, followed by a number of details. Decide which details should be included in a paragraph which uses the topic sentence. Cross out details which should not be included. Give a reason why you have chosen to discard each detail.

TOPIC SENTENCE: My favorite place to visit is the beach.

DETAILS:

1. The water is very warm even in the early summer.

2. There is a bird museum at the beach.

3. The bird museum has pictures of birds that you can see along the shore and in the trees.

4. I enjoy looking for different kinds of birds.

5. There are carnival rides at the beach.

6. I don't like the hot dogs sold at the cafeteria at the beach.

7. The beach is never crowded with people.

8. I like playing in the sand.

9. Sometimes crabs come out of their holes in the sand and play in the water.

10. I really like swimming in the waves and body surfing.

11. I like to be around many people when I am on holidays.

12. There are many shells at the beach, and I can make things from them.

13. My mother and father let me stay up later in the summer.

14. Sometimes we have a barbecue at the beach and I really like the hamburgers my dad makes there.

15. When it rains there is not much to do at the beach.

16. Being outside in the sunshine gives me a good appetite at lunch time.

17. My older sister lets me bury her in the sand up to her neck.

EXERCISES IN UNITY (Continued)

C) The topic sentence for a paragraph is given below, followed by a number of details. Decide which details should be included in a paragraph which uses the topic sentence. Cross out details which should not be included. Give a reason why you have chosen to discard each detail.

TOPIC SENTENCE: Toronto is a city which combines both the old and the new.

DETAILS:

1. Toronto's skyscrapers made of metal, stone and glass dominate the skyline.

2. The population of Toronto is now more than three million.

3. Casa Loma, built by Sir Henry Pellatt in the early part of this century, has 98 rooms and secret underground passages.

4. Skydome, the home of the Toronto Blue Jays, looks like a giant oyster with a huge shell which opens and closes.

5. The Art Gallery of Ontario is one of North America's largest art museums.

6. A cruise in the harbor can be lots of fun.

7. Ontario Place covers almost 100 acres and houses modern buildings like the Cinesphere among quaint ethnic restaurants.

8. The Ontario Parliament Buildings in Queen's Park were built at the end of the nineteenth century.

9. The roof of the Parliament Buildings is made of green copper.

10. The C.N. Tower is the tallest free-standing structure in the world.

11. The C.N. Tower restaurant provides a spectacular view of the city and the harbor below.

12. I enjoy going to the Canadian National Exhibition, which is now over 100 years old.

13. The best ride at Canada's Wonderland is Top Gun which is a looping, inverted roller coaster.

14. Shopping at the Eaton Center can take up most of a day.

EXERCISES IN UNITY (Continued)

D) The topic sentence for a paragraph is given below, followed by a number of details. Decide which details should be included in a paragraph which uses the topic sentence. Cross out details which should not be included. Give a reason why you have chosen to discard each detail.

TOPIC SENTENCE: On the bus next to me sat the strangest looking person I have ever seen.

DETAILS:

1. She carried a large shopping bag loaded with fireworks and another one with groceries.

2. She had long, red hair which stood up all over her head.

3. Her nails were painted purple and green.

4. She looked like she was over 100 years old.

5. She had a wart on her chin and the wart was covered with hairs.

6. She stared straight ahead and did not say a word.

7. Her orange and green floor-length dress had long sleeves, but it was ripped and tattered.

8. On her cheek, she had a tattoo of a rose and an airplane.

9. She got on the bus at Maple Street and got off at Simcoe Hall.

10. She kept on scratching her neck, as if she had fleas.

11. In her purse was a large clock which chimed the hour just after she sat down.

12. As she breathed in and out, she gasped for air.

13. She looked like she was enjoying the ride on the bus.

14. She wore new white tennis shoes.

15. On her left hand were six or seven rings, but she wore no rings on her right hand.

16. Her cheeks were sunken and pale.

17. She wore purple eye shadow.

EXERCISES IN TOPIC SENTENCE

A) The topic sentence for a paragraph is given below. In the space provided, add five specific details which would create an interesting paragraph. Make sure that each detail is included in the idea expressed in the topic sentence.

TOPIC SENTENCE: Margaret possesses all the qualities of a good friend.

DETAILS:

1. _____

   _____

   _____

2. _____

   _____

   _____

3. _____

   _____

   _____

4. _____

   _____

   _____

5. _____

   _____

   _____

EXERCISES IN TOPIC SENTENCE (Continued)

B) The topic sentence for a paragraph is given below. In the space provided, add five specific details which would create an interesting paragraph. Make sure that each detail is included in the idea expressed in the topic sentence.

TOPIC SENTENCE: Swimming can be both a fun activity and also a good way to build a healthy body.

DETAILS:

1. _____

   _____

   _____

2. _____

   _____

   _____

3. _____

   _____

   _____

4. _____

   _____

   _____

5. _____

   _____

   _____

EXERCISES IN TOPIC SENTENCE (continued)

C) The topic sentence for a paragraph is given below. In the space provided, add five specific details which would create an interesting paragraph. Make sure that each detail is included in the idea expressed in the topic sentence.

TOPIC SENTENCE: On my first day, I knew that I would be happy (or unhappy) in my new school.

DETAILS:

1. _____

_____

_____

2. _____

_____

_____

3. _____

_____

_____

4. _____

_____

_____

5. _____

_____

_____

EXERCISES IN TOPIC SENTENCE (Continued)

D) The topic sentence for a paragraph is given below. In the space provided, add five specific details which would create an interesting paragraph. Make sure that each detail is included in the idea expressed in the topic sentence.

TOPIC SENTENCE: Travel broadens a person's mind by presenting new experiences and new ways to think about the world.

DETAILS:

1. _____

_____

_____

2. _____

_____

_____

3. _____

_____

_____

4. _____

_____

_____

5. _____

_____

_____

EXERCISES IN TOPIC SENTENCE (Continued)

E) The topic sentence for a paragraph is given below. In the space provided, add five specific details which would create an interesting paragraph. Make sure that each detail is included in the idea expressed in the topic sentence.

TOPIC SENTENCE: My favorite activity is one which allows me to have fun while I learn new skills.

DETAILS:

1. _____

   _____

   _____

2. _____

   _____

   _____

3. _____

   _____

   _____

4. _____

   _____

   _____

5. _____

   _____

   _____

EXERCISES IN TOPIC SENTENCE (Continued)

F) The topic sentence for a paragraph is given below. In the space provided, add five specific details which would create an interesting paragraph. Make sure that each detail is included in the idea expressed in the topic sentence.

> TOPIC SENTENCE: My favorite television show/movie/music (choose one) makes me dream about new experiences which life can offer me.

DETAILS:

1. _____

_____

_____

2. _____

_____

_____

3. _____

_____

_____

4. _____

_____

_____

5. _____

_____

_____

EXERCISES IN TOPIC SENTENCE (Continued)

G) A topic sentence must be **general** enough to include all the ideas in the paragraph, but **limiting** enough to allow the writer to focus on specifics. That sounds like a contradiction, doesn't it? That is why writing is not an easy task; the writer must decide what is too general or what is too limiting. If the topic sentence is too general, it might be more useful for a longer piece of writing. On the other hand, a topic sentence which is too narrow may lead to a very short paragraph. For each pair of possible topic sentences given below, choose which would be more useful in writing a paragraph.

1. a) There are many interesting shows on television.

    b) Television emphasizes too much violence.

2. a) Collecting stamps is a good activity for people of all ages.

    b) Stamps for a collection can be found in the most unlikely places.

3. a) Quebec City can be a fun place to visit.

    b) There are many things to do in Quebec City during its annual Winter Carnival.

4. a) Basketball is a good sport.

    b) Basketball is good exercise.

5. a) A dog is a pet which every family should own.

    b) A dog can be trained to do many tricks.

6. a) *Jurassic Park: The Lost World* is an excellent movie.

    b) *Jurassic Park: The Lost World* is both exciting and fun to watch.

EXERCISES IN TOPIC SENTENCE (Continued)

H) Write a topic sentence which covers all the details which follow. Remember that your topic sentence must be **general** enough to include all the ideas, but **limiting** enough to allow the writer to focus on specifics.

TOPIC SENTENCE: _____

_____

_____

_____

DETAILS:

1. My hands shook a little as I opened the door of the large, imposing building.

2. I peered inside, not knowing what to expect.

3. As my eyes became more accustomed to the dim light, I saw a room covered in dust and cobwebs.

4. Cobwebs clung to the huge chandelier which hung over the staircase.

5. I closed the door behind me and inched my way to the foot of the stairs.

6. The stairs began to creak as I slowly ascended them, wondering who the last person was to ascend the stairs and whether I would ever come down them again.

7. Then I heard a blood-curdling scream and ran as quickly as I could out of the building.

8. That was the last time I would ever enter that house alone.

EXERCISES IN TOPIC SENTENCE (Continued)

I) Write a topic sentence which covers all the details which follow. Remember that your topic sentence must be **general** enough to include all the ideas, but **limiting** enough to allow the writer to focus on specifics.

TOPIC SENTENCE: _____

_____

_____

_____

DETAILS:

1. She worked me middling hard for about an hour and then the window made her ease up.

2. I couldn't stood it much longer.

3. Then for an hour it was deadly dull, and I was fidgety.

4. Miss Watson would say, "Don't put your feet up there, Huckleberry"; and "Don't scrunch up like that, Huckleberry--set up straight"; and pretty soon she would say, "Don't gap and stretch like that, Huckleberry--why don't you try to behave?"

5. Then she told me all about the bad place and I said I wished I was there.

6. She got mad then but I didn't mean no harm.

7. All I wanted was to go somewheres; all I wanted was a change, I warn't particular.

8. She said it was wicked to say what I said, said she wouldn't say it for the whole world, she was going to live so as to go to the good place.

9. Well, I couldn't see no advantage in going where she was going, so I made up my mind I wouldn't try for it.

10. But I never said so, because it would only make trouble and wouldn't do no good.

(from <u>Huckleberry Finn</u> by Mark Twain)

EXERCISES IN TOPIC SENTENCE (Continued)

J) Write a topic sentence which covers all the details which follow. Remember that your topic sentence must be **general** enough to include all the ideas, but **limiting** enough to allow the writer to focus on specifics.

TOPIC SENTENCE: _____

_____

_____

_____

DETAILS:

1. He knew no greater delight than to sit conning books of romance and chivalry, tales of high adventure and gallant deeds of knight-errantry, encounters of heroes and giants, and all the marvelous actions of the legendary warriors of old.

2. The more he read the more he longed to read.

3. He was, as it were, steeped in books of chivalry.

4. Yet he gave ever more and more time to this, his best loved pursuit.

5. He even gave up coursing and hunting, and sold many good acres of his land in order to buy volumes of romance, in which for days together he would bury himself, blind and deaf to all around him.

(from <u>Don Quixote</u> by Miguel de Cervantes)

EXERCISES IN TOPIC SENTENCE (Continued)

K) Write a topic sentence which covers all the details which follow. Remember than your topic sentence must be **general** enough to include all the ideas, but **limiting** enough to allow the writer to focus on specifics.

TOPIC SENTENCE: _____

_____

_____

_____

DETAILS:

1. The streets were narrow and covered with snow and ice for most of the year.

2. There were really only about four or five streets in the little town and so in winter there was nowhere to drive the car except out of town.

3. The houses were wooden and poorly insulated, obviously erected very cheaply for the workers at the mill.

4. Sulphur dioxide filled the air with the smell of rotten eggs that clung to your clothes, your hair and your skin.

5. This gas was produced as a by-product of the pulp and paper industry which controlled all aspects of the town's life.

6. If anything good was to come of living in this little northern town it would not come from the roads, the buildings, or even the air itself.

EXERCISES IN TOPIC SENTENCE (Continued)

L) Write a topic sentence which covers all the details which follow. Remember that your topic sentence must be **general** enough to include all the ideas, but **limiting** enough to allow the writer to focus on specifics.

TOPIC SENTENCE: _____

_____

_____

_____

DETAILS:

1. The Duckling was forced to swim about in the water, to prevent the surface from freezing entirely.

2. But every night the hole in which it swam about became smaller and smaller.

3. It froze so hard that the icy covering crackled again.

4. The Duckling was obliged to use its legs continually to prevent the hole from freezing up.

5. At last it became exhausted, and lay quite still, and thus froze fast in the ice.

(from <u>The Ugly Duckling</u> by Hans Christian Andersen)

EXERCISES IN TOPIC SENTENCE (Continued)

M) Write a topic sentence which covers all the details which follow. Remember that your topic sentence must be **general** enough to include all the ideas, but **limiting** enough to allow the writer to focus on specifics.

TOPIC SENTENCE: _____

_____

_____

_____

DETAILS:

1. Mr. Arrow had no command among the men, and people did what they pleased with him.

2. But that was by no means the worst of it.

3. After a day or two at sea he began to appear on deck with hazy eye, red cheeks, stuttering tongue, and other marks of drunkenness.

4. Time after time he was ordered below in disgrace.

5. Sometimes he fell and cut himself.

6. Sometimes he lay all day long in his little bunk at one side of the companion.

7. Sometimes for a day or two he would be almost sober and attend to his work at least passably.

(from <u>Treasure Island</u> by Robert Louis Stevenson)

COHERENCE

Coherence is a smooth movement from one idea to the next in a paragraph. In order to achieve coherence a writer must pay attention to two things.

1. arrangement of the ideas
2. logical connection between ideas

Arrangement of Ideas:

When you build a house, you cannot put the roof on before the walls are built. Similarly, in a paragraph, you cannot skip around from one idea to the next without any sort of arrangement of these ideas; otherwise the reader may become lost or confused.

There are several ways to arrange ideas in a paragraph:

1. chronological order: This means that the ideas are presented in the same order that they occurred in time. We have all heard people tell stories when they omit an important event and then go back to put it in later; this can be very confusing. The writer has the advantage that he or she can revise the writing, make any changes before the copy is finished and ready for the reader. So the writer can put in any information which he or she has forgotten.

2. physical order: This means that the ideas, particularly in a description, are placed in some kind of order of space, such as left to right, top to bottom, or outside to inside.

3. order of importance: The writer can begin with the most important idea and lead to the least important idea. Or the writer can begin with the least important idea and lead to the most important idea. Order of importance can be very helpful when the writer is trying to convince the reader of a particular point of view.

4. order of climax: The writer can build suspense leading to a climax. This type of order is similar to the order of importance in that the climax (the most important idea) is put last.

Whatever order the writer chooses, it is important that the sentences in the paragraph be arranged in a logical sequence, so that one idea follows another.

COHERENCE (Continued)

Logical Connection between Ideas:

A train may have all the right cars which are put in the best order for pulling them. However, if the cars are not connected to each other, the train will not be able to move them.

There are words which we use in English called **transition** words. Transition words provide the connection between the sentences, just as the coupling on a train provides the connection between its cars.

The most obvious transition words list ideas in the order in which they appear. These are "number" words, such as:

- first
- secondly
- thirdly, etc.

These words are very obvious transitions and would be avoided by more experienced writers.

Transition words can express the order of arrangement chosen by the writer. Therefore, there can be transition words which mean each of the following:

- time
- physical order
- order of importance
- similar ideas
- different ideas
- conclusion

The chart on page 24 provides examples of transition words which can express each of these types of arrangement.

COHERENCE (Continued)

Chart: Examples of Transition Words

Type of Arrangement	Examples	
Time	then later during now presently	next before afterwards meanwhile eventually
Physical Order	to the right above under in the distance straight ahead	to the left below beside
Order of Importance	more importantly to some degree to a lesser extent	
Similar Ideas	in addition also and in the same way	similarly likewise moreover
Different Ideas	on the other hand on the contrary however nevertheless yet	but otherwise still
Conclusion	therefore so for this reason	thus hence

These are only some of the many transitions or connecting words available in English.

EXERCISES IN COHERENCE

A) In small groups decide what kind of order (chronological order, physical order, order of importance, order of climax) would work best for a paragraph on each of the following topics. Provide two good reasons for choosing each kind of order.

1. a story about a visit to a haunted house:

   kind of order: _____

   reasons: a) _____

   b) _____

2. a description of the haunted house:

   kind of order: _____

   reasons: a) _____

   b) _____

3. a paragraph persuading your parents to let you stay up later:

   kind of order: _____

   reasons: a) _____

   b) _____

4. a paragraph about the causes of the American Revolution:

   kind of order: _____

   reasons: a) _____

   b) _____

EXERCISES IN COHERENCE (Continued)

B) In small groups decide what kind of order (**chronological order, physical order, order of importance, order of climax**) would work best for a paragraph on each of the following topics. Provide two good reasons for choosing each kind of order.

1. a description of the layout of a Zoo you have visited:

   kind of order: _____

   reasons: a) _____

   b) _____

2. an explanation of the events which occurred on the way to school:

   kind of order: _____

   reasons: a) _____

   b) _____

3. a paragraph describing your best friend:

   kind of order: _____

   reasons: a) _____

   b) _____

4. an explanation of how to make a peanut butter sandwich:

   kind of order: _____

   reasons: a) _____

   b) _____

EXERCISES IN COHERENCE (Continued)

C) The topic sentence for a paragraph is given below, followed by a number of details. Decide the order in which the details should appear in the paragraph. Then write the paragraph providing any necessary transition words.

TOPIC SENTENCE: On the bus next to me sat the strangest looking person I have ever seen.

DETAILS:

1. She carried a large shopping bag loaded with fireworks and another one with groceries.

2. She had long, red hair which stood up all over her head.

3. Her nails were painted purple and green.

4. She looked like she was over 100 years old.

5. She had a wart on her chin and the wart was covered with hairs.

6. She stared straight ahead and did not say a word.

7. Her orange and green floor-length dress had long sleeves, but it was ripped and tattered.

8. On her cheek, she had a tattoo of a rose and an airplane.

9. She kept on scratching her neck, as if she had fleas.

10. In her purse was a large clock which chimed the hour just after she sat down.

11. As she breathed in and out, she gasped for air.

12. She wore new white tennis shoes.

13. On her left hand were six or seven rings, but she wore no rings on her right hand.

14. Her cheeks were sunken and pale.

15. She wore purple eye shadow.

ORDER: Write the sentence number in sequence: _____ _____ _____ _____

_____ _____ _____ _____ _____ _____ _____ _____

Write the paragraph on another sheet of paper.

EXERCISES IN COHERENCE (Continued)

D) The topic sentence for a paragraph is given below, followed by a number of details. Decide the order in which the details should appear in the paragraph. Then write the paragraph providing any necessary transition words.

> **TOPIC SENTENCE:** Sam is one of the best players on the baseball team.

DETAILS:

1. Sam is a good athlete.

2. Sam is very tall for his age.

3. Sam hit two home runs in the last game.

4. When the pitcher throws the ball, Sam has a good eye and can determine where the ball will go in relation to the plate.

5. Sam can run to first base faster than anyone on the team.

6. Sam can pitch, hit and catch very well.

7. Sam is a very good player at first base or short stop.

8. Sam can read the pitcher very well and knows when he should attempt to steal a base.

9. One day when our team was losing, Sam hit a grand-slam home-run, which allowed us to win the game.

ORDER: Write the sentence number in sequence: _____ _____ _____ _____

_____ _____ _____ _____ _____

Write the paragraph on another sheet of paper.

EXERCISES IN COHERENCE (Continued)

E) The topic sentence for a paragraph is given below, followed by a number of details. Decide the order in which the details should appear in the paragraph. Then write the paragraph providing any necessary transition words.

TOPIC SENTENCE: My favorite place to visit is the beach.

DETAILS:

1. The water is very warm even in the early summer.

2. There is a bird museum at the beach.

3. The bird museum has pictures of birds that you can see along the shore and in the trees.

4. I enjoy looking for different kinds of birds.

5. There are carnival rides at the beach.

6. The beach is never crowded with people.

7. I like playing in the sand.

8. Sometimes crabs come out of their holes in the sand and play in the water.

9. I really like swimming in the waves and body surfing.

10. There are many shells at the beach, and I can make things from them.

11. Sometimes we have a barbecue at the beach and I really like the hamburgers my dad makes there.

12. Being outside in the sunshine gives me a good appetite at lunch time.

13. My older sister lets me bury her in the sand up to her neck.

ORDER: Write the sentence number in sequence. _____ _____ _____ _____

_____ _____ _____ _____ _____ _____ _____ _____ _____

Write the paragraph on another sheet of paper.

EXERCISES IN COHERENCE (Continued)

F) The topic sentence for a paragraph is given below, followed by a number of details. Decide the order in which the details should appear in the paragraph. Then write the paragraph providing any necessary transition words.

TOPIC SENTENCE: Toronto is a city which combines both the old and the new.

DETAILS:

1. Toronto's skyscrapers made of metal, stone and glass dominate the skyline.

2. Casa Loma, built by Sir Henry Pellatt in the early part of this century, has 98 rooms and secret underground passages.

3. Skydome, the home of the Toronto Blue Jays, looks like a giant oyster with a huge shell which opens and closes.

4. Ontario Place covers almost 100 acres and houses modern buildings like the Cinesphere among quaint ethnic restaurants.

5. The Ontario Parliament Buildings in Queen's Park were built at the end of the nineteenth century.

6. The roof of the Parliament Buildings is made of green copper.

7. The C.N. Tower is the tallest free-standing structure in the world.

ORDER: Write the sentence number in sequence: _____ _____ _____

_____ _____ _____ _____

Write the paragraph on another sheet of paper.

EXERCISES IN CONCLUDING SENTENCE

A) A concluding sentence should sum up the main idea of the paragraph, but it should not merely restate the words of the topic sentence. A good writer will try to clinch the idea in a strong statement.

Write a good concluding sentence for the following paragraph. Then share your ideas with your classmates. Decide on the most effective concluding sentence written by your class.

Taking the train can be an exhilarating experience. I love to look out the window at the countryside as the train chugs along. Sometimes I imagine that I live in one of those wayward farms, small villages or large cities. I wonder how my life would be changed in any of those places. Yes, I can see the same things from a car window, but I never really have time to sit and think, time to imagine what life might be like in some other place. Would it be a better life or one which only leads to more troubles? I also like to be able to get up and wander around. I may have difficulty keeping my balance as the train moves from side to side, but that is all part of the fun. Similarly, I appreciate going into the dining car and sitting down to have a meal or just a glass of coke. You can't do that in a car; you have to stop at some restaurant along the way and sometimes battle the crowds. Finally, I like the people I meet on the train--a strange assortment from all walks of life.

Concluding sentence: _____

_____

_____

_____

EXERCISES IN CONCLUDING SENTENCE
(Continued)

B) A concluding sentence should sum up the main idea of the paragraph, but it should not merely restate the words of the topic sentence. A good writer will try to clinch the idea in a strong statement.

Write a good concluding sentence for the following paragraph. Then share your ideas with your classmates. Decide on the most effective concluding sentence written by your class.

One day when there was a good deal of kicking, my mother whinnied to me to come to her, and then she said, "I wish you to pay attention to what I am going to say to you. The colts who live here are very good colts, but they are cart-horse colts, and, of course, they have not learned manners. You have been well bred and well born. Your father has a great name in these parts, and your grandfather won the cup two years at the Newmarket races; your grandmother had the sweetest temper of any horse I ever knew, and I think you have never seen me kick or bite. I hope you will grow up gentle and good, and never learn bad ways. Do your work with a will, lift your feet up well when you trot, and never bite or kick even in play."

(from Black Beauty by Anna Sewell)

Concluding sentence: _____

_____

_____

_____

EXERCISES IN CONCLUDING SENTENCE
(Continued)

C) A concluding sentence should sum up the main idea of the paragraph, but it should not merely restate the words of the topic sentence. A good writer will try to clinch the idea in a strong statement.

Write a good concluding sentence for the following paragraph. Then share your ideas with your classmates. Decide on the most effective concluding sentence written by your class.

It was not in the first few moments that I saw all these things, though I saw more of them in the first moments than might be supposed. But I saw that everything within my view which ought to be white had been white long ago, and had lost its luster, and was faded to yellow. I saw that the bride within the bridal dress had withered like the dress, and like the flowers, and had no brightness left but the brightness of her sunken eyes. I saw that the dress had been put upon the rounded figure of a young woman, and that the figure upon which it now hung loose had shrunk to skin and bone. Once, I had been taken to see some ghastly waxwork at the fair, representing I know not what impossible personage lying in state. Once, I had been taken to one of our old marsh churches to see a skeleton in the ashes of a rich dress, that had been dug out of a vault under the church pavement. Now, waxwork and skeleton seemed to have dark eyes that moved and looked at me.

(from <u>Great Expectations</u> by Charles Dickens)

Concluding sentence: _____

_____

_____

_____

TYPES OF PARAGRAPHS

Three major types of paragraphs are dealt with in this resource:

· exposition
· narration
· description

Each of these three types of writing has a different purpose, and therefore each one is planned and constructed differently.

Type of Paragraph	Definition	Purpose
Exposition	a detailed explanation which involves facts or opinions	· to explain or inform · to convince or persuade
Narration	a story with a plot, setting and characters	· to entertain · to inform or teach a lesson
Description	a detailed picture of the characteristics of an object, person or place	· to inform · to entertain

The writer of a paragraph must decide what type of paragraph he or she is writing. This will depend on the topic chosen and the purpose of the assignment. Students should note that many pieces of writing involve characteristics of all three types: A short story, for example, may include explanation (that is, exposition) and description. Similarly, an exposition may develop part of its explanation by telling a story or may use description. However, for most assignments in school, students will not go wrong if they decide to use one of these types of paragraphs.

Before beginning to write, students should ask themselves:

· What is the purpose of the writing assignment?
· What type of paragraph will best achieve this purpose?

Often the question or assignment will make this decision for the student. The assignment may be, for example, to write a short story or to write an explanation.

TYPES OF PARAGAPHS (Continued)

EXERCISE 1 ON TYPES OF PARAGRAPHS

In the chart which follows, you are given a topic for a paragraph. You are to decide what type of paragraph--exposition, narration or description--you would write for each topic. Then jot down ideas you could use to write a paragraph on the particular topic. The type of paragraph you choose will determine the ideas you use; therefore, for some of these topics, you could write any of the three types of paragraph.

Topic	Type of Paragraph	Ideas
1. The Place I Would Most Like to Visit		
2. My Pet		
3. Thomas Edison		

TYPES OF PARAGRAPHS (Continued)

EXERCISE 2 ON TYPES OF PARAGRAPHS

In the chart which follows, you are given a topic for a paragraph. You are to decide what type of paragraph--exposition, **narration** or **description**--you would write for each topic. Then jot down ideas you could use to write a paragraph on the particular topic. The type of paragraph you choose will determine the ideas you use; therefore, for some of these topics, you could write any of the three types of paragraph.

Topic	Type of Paragraph	Ideas
1. The Best Story I Have Ever Read		
2. My Hero		
3. The War Zone		

TYPES OF PARAGRAPHS (Continued)

EXERCISE 3 ON TYPES OF PARAGRAPHS

In the chart which follows, you are given a topic for a paragraph. You are to decide what ideas you could use to write each type of paragraph on this topic--exposition, **narration** or **description**. Write down ideas you could use in the space provided in the chart. You may limit the topic of you wish.

TOPIC: The Zoo (or The Circus or The Amusement Park)

Exposition	Narration	Description

TYPES OF PARAGRAPHS (Continued)

EXERCISE 4 ON TYPES OF PARAGRAPHS

In the chart which follows, you are given a topic for a paragraph. You are to decide what ideas you could use to write each type of paragraph on this topic--exposition, narration or description. Write down ideas you could use in the space provided in the chart. You may limit the topic of you wish.

TOPIC: My Favorite Relative

Exposition	Narration	Description

TYPES OF PARAGRAPHS (Continued)

AN EXAMPLE OF AN EXPOSITORY PARAGRAPH

Remember that an **exposition** tries to explain things. Sometimes the explanation can be persuasive, as the author has attempted to do in the following paragraph:

Michelangelo

Although Michelangelo is very famous as a painter whose masterpiece is the ceiling of the Sistine Chapel in Vatican City, perhaps his greatest works are his sculptures. Artists in the time period before Michelangelo's birth in 1475 painted or created statues of religious scenes; but their paintings and statues were more like stick figures than real human beings. Michelangelo's statues show people with muscles and veins, real bodies on real people. Moses, a statue which today is displayed in the Church of St. Peter-in-Chains in Rome, shows a strong man who survived many years living in the desert. Moses is very muscular and looks healthy enough to live through the hardships of his life. Even Mary, one of the two figures in the Pieta found in the Vatican, is a strong and muscular woman as she needed to be to live almost 30 years after the death of her son. But perhaps Michelangelo's greatest work of art is David, a statue which we can see today in the Academia in Florence, Italy. In The Bible, David was a young boy who killed the giant, Goliath, with a stone. A statue of David by Donatello shows a thin, weak little boy with a grin on his face. But Michelangelo's David shows a strong and muscular young man with a look of determination on his face; his David killed a giant with a stone. Because his statues depict the strong human beings that would have existed, Michelangelo shows his genius in his sculptures.

Notice that this **expository** paragraph presents an argument about Michelangelo and then explains reasons why the argument is a valid one. The argument is expressed in the first sentence, which is also the topic sentence, and is restated in the concluding sentence.

TYPES OF PARAGRAPHS (Continued)

EXERCISE ON THE EXPOSITORY PARAGRAPH

Read the paragraph *Michelangelo* on page 39 and then answer the following questions:

1. Begin by understanding the vocabulary. What is the meaning of each of the following words:

   - masterpiece
   - stick figures
   - determination
   - depict
   - existed

2. What is the argument which the writer is expressing in this paragraph?

3. Where in this paragraph is the argument stated directly?

4. What is the topic sentence of the paragraph?

5. To make an effective argument, a writer uses examples. What are the three examples used in this paragraph?

6. What idea is common to all three examples?

7. Provide examples of three transition words used in the paragraph. Explain how each transition word links two ideas together.

8. Choose three words from this paragraph and explain why each one is a good choice to express the idea.

TYPES OF PARAGRAPHS (Continued)

AN EXAMPLE OF A DESCRIPTIVE PARAGRAPH

Remember that a **description** tries to present a detailed picture. The following paragraph is taken from <u>Anne of Green Gables</u> by Lucy Maud Montgomery.

Anne's First View of Green Gables

She opened her eyes and looked about her. They were on a crest of a hill. The sun had set some time since, but the landscape was still clear in the mellow afterlight. To the west a dark church spire rose up against a marigold sky. Below was a little valley and beyond a long, gently rising slope with snug farmsteads scattered along it. From one to another the child's eyes darted, eager and wistful. At last they lingered on one away to the left, far back from the road, dimly white with blossoming trees in the twilight of the surrounding woods. Over it, in the stainless southwest sky, a great crystal-white star was shining like a lamp of guidance and promise.

Notice that this **descriptive** paragraph list various details to provide to the reader a vivid picture of what Anne sees. Look at the specific nouns which are used and the adjectives which described them.

TYPES OF PARAGRAPHS (Continued)

EXERCISE ON THE DESCRIPTIVE PARAGRAPH

Read the paragraph *Anne's First View of Green Gables* on page 41 and then answer the following questions:

1. Begin by understanding the vocabulary. What is the meaning of each of the following words:

    - crest
    - afterlight
    - marigold
    - wistful
    - twilight
    - crystal

    - mellow
    - spire
    - snug
    - lingered
    - stainless

2. List the details of the view in the order that Lucy Maud Montgomery described them in the paragraph.

3. Make a list of all the nouns used in the paragraph. Which ones are particularly easy for the reader to picture? Which ones are specific rather than general?

4. Make a list of all the adjectives used in the paragraph. Which ones help to provide a vivid picture in the reader's mind?

5. Why is **marigold** a better word to use than **orange**?

6. Why is **stainless** more effective than **clear**?

7. There are also some good verbs used here. Why are the following good examples: **scattered, darted, lingered**?

TYPES OF PARAGRAPHS (Continued)

AN EXAMPLE OF A NARRATIVE PARAGRAPH

Remember that a **narrative** tell a story. A single paragraph story should be very simple; a longer story would require more than one paragraph. Notice that the following story does not begin with Once upon a time.

The Bees

I sat motionless in the field surrounded by bees. I had come there with my family for a quiet picnic. But now I was in danger--or so I thought. There must have been fifteen bees around me. I couldn't turn my head to count them all. I remembered that someone once told me that bees won't sting a person unless they feel that they will be harmed, so I continued to sit as still as possible. "All right, bees," I thought, "you've had your fun in scaring me. Now go and find some flowers to make your honey." Suddenly a bee landed on my nose. I screwed my eyes to look at it, but otherwise I didn't move a muscle. Then another one slowly buzzed by my eyes. I still didn't move. "Please, bees, please leave me alone," I said to myself. Then came the greatest terror of all. Something was moving up my leg between my socks and my shorts. It was slimy and cold, but I couldn't move to look at it. "I hate snakes," Indiana Jones once said in a movie--and I agree with him. Suddenly, without any apparent reason, the bee flew from my nose and into the distance, followed by his fellow hive-keepers. I jumped up and the snake fell to the ground. It was a harmless garter snake. What a relief? I ran back to join my family. I will always remember that family picnic which was supposed to be so quiet and relaxed.

Notice that this **narrative** paragraph tells a story which builds to a climax. Because the story is written in only one paragraph, it tells of only one brief incident, gives little description of setting or character, but ones conclude. To arouse the reader's interest it starts in the middle of the action.

TYPES OF PARAGRAPHS (Continued)

EXERCISE ON THE NARRATIVE PARAGRAPH

Read the paragraph *The Bees* on page 43 and then answer the following questions:

1. Begin by understanding the vocabulary. What is the meaning of each of the following words?

   · motionless
   · terror
   · slimy
   · apparent
   · garter snake

2. Why is it a good idea to begin the story the way this author has, rather than saying, *One day my family went on a picnic?*

3. How many incidents are narrated in this story? Why are there not more incidents related?

4. List in order the events which the author of the paragraph has chosen to include.

5. What sentence is the climax or high point of interest and tension in this paragraph?

6. Is the concluding sentence a good one? Explain why you think it is a good one or why you think it is a poor choice.

7. Choose three words from this paragraph and explain why each one is a good choice to express the idea.

8. Are there any words in this paragraph which are not very good choices? Which words would be better choices?

USING THE WRITING PROCESS

The writing process is not new to schools in North America. Today, students learn to use the writing process as soon as they begin to learn to write. Much of what is said here, then, will be nothing new to teachers of writing. However, perhaps isolating the procedure on the next few pages will help teachers to teach and students to learn.

The writing process consists of four major steps:

- prewriting
- writing the first draft
- editing and revising
- writing the final copy

Steps 2 and 3 may be repeated as many times as necessary; the student may write, edit and revise successive drafts until he or she is satisfied with the work. D.H. Lawrence, the distinguished novelist, wrote seven drafts of his masterpiece, <u>Sons and Lovers</u>, and was still not completely satisfied.

USING THE WRITING PROCESS (Continued)

PREWRITING

It is very difficult to sit down and write effectively without doing any preplanning. Many educators consider the first stage of the writing process to be the most important.

Prewriting consists of four parts:

- Brainstorming
- Research
- Selection of ideas to be used
- Prewriting Plan.

1. BRAINSTORMING

The first stage of the writing process, after choosing the topic, is the brainstorming stage. The purpose of this stage is to use what the student already knows to begin to compile information which will be used for the final draft.

At the brainstorming stage, the student writes down on a piece of paper any information which pertains to the topic as these ideas come into his or her mind. The student may use mind-mapping techniques if these are easier.

The next four pages show sheets which may be used for brainstorming each of the three types of paragraphs in this resource:

- the exposition
- the narrative
- description.

Teachers may use these sheets or devise their own. It is important, however, that students be given some guidance to teach them techniques for brainstorming. The teacher should not assume that students already know how to do this.

USING THE WRITING PROCESS (Continued)

PREWRITING

BRAINSTORMING AN EXPOSITION

TOPIC: What do you intend to explain?

_____

_____

Fill in the chart with as much information as you know.

Who is involved?	What is involved?
Where did it take place?	**When did it take place?**
How did it happen?	**What events occurred?**

USING THE WRITING PROCESS (Continued)

PREWRITING

BRAINSTORMING A NARRATIVE (Part 1)

Fill in the chart with your first ideas.

List five possible settings for a story (time and place):

1.

2.

3.

4.

5.

Briefly describe five possible characters who interest you (name and short description):

1.

2.

3.

4.

5.

List five possible events which could occur to one or more of these characters in one or more of the settings you have listed:

1.

2.

3.

4.

5.

USING THE WRITING PROCESS (Continued)

PREWRITING

BRAINSTORMING A NARRATIVE (Part 2)

Fill in the chart with ideas chosen from completing part 1.

List the setting you will use for your story (time and place):

Describe the setting:

Choose the central character for your story. State his or her name and provide a short description of the character's appearance and personality:

List other characters you may use:

Choose an event which will occur. List the sequence of events which will take place:

USING THE WRITING PROCESS (Continued)

PREWRITING

BRAINSTORMING A DESCRIPTION

TOPIC: What or whom do you intend to describe?

_____

_____

In the center of this page, do a mind-map, starting with what the person, place or object that you intend to describe looks like. If you are describing a person, add a section on the personality.

USING THE WRITING PROCESS (Continued)

PREWRITING

2. RESEARCH

Research may not be required in the types of student writing presented in this resource. Certain assignments may only require brainstorming.

However, research may be required for any of the following reasons:

- The student is writing an exposition on a topic unknown to him or her, a topic which is not considered common knowledge, such as *The Wright Brothers* or a country which he or she has never visited.

- The student is writing a short story set in a particular place or time and needs to know more about that place or time.

- The student is writing a factual description about someone or something with which he or she is not familiar.

Teachers often assume that students know how to research. Quite often, students simply copy information from an encyclopedia. They need to be taught how to do research well. The teacher should stress the following techniques:

- Students should read the encyclopedia, textbook or whatever source and then try to express the ideas in their own words. This will check to see that students are really understanding what they have read.

- Students should prepare a list of relevant questions (or the teacher may provide such a list). The kinds of questions asked in the brainstorming sheets on pages 47 to 50 of this resource could be helpful. Alternatively, students could ask simple questions such as: Who? When? Where? How? Why?

- Students should be cautioned not to write down every word they read. As they put the ideas into their own words, they should also select the information that seems to be important and only write that down.

- Students should note the source of all information they are writing down. Particularly in the higher grades, students will need to provide these sources with their finished writing.

USING THE WRITING PROCESS (Continued)

PREWRITING

3. SELECTION OF IDEAS TO BE USED:

After completing the brainstorming and research, the student should have many ideas for the paragraph. Now is the time to start selecting the ideas which will actually be used and to organize them in some logical form.

Perhaps the easiest way for students to do this is to follow this pattern:

- Group the ideas that are similar. Each grouping will eventually form one part of the paragraph.

- Eliminate any ideas which do not seem to be useful. If the paragraph seems very long, perhaps even useful ideas may have to be eliminated. Select the most important ideas to use in the first draft.

- If there are parts which need more detail, add the detail at this stage.

4. PREWRITING PLAN:

The Prewriting Plan may be the most important step in any piece of writing. If it is done well, the prewriting plan shows the entire composition on one sheet of paper. (Students should use larger sheets of paper for long or more complicated pieces of writing, but shorter pieces should fit on one $8\frac{1}{2}$ " by 11" sheet.)

An example of a prewriting plan is shown below.

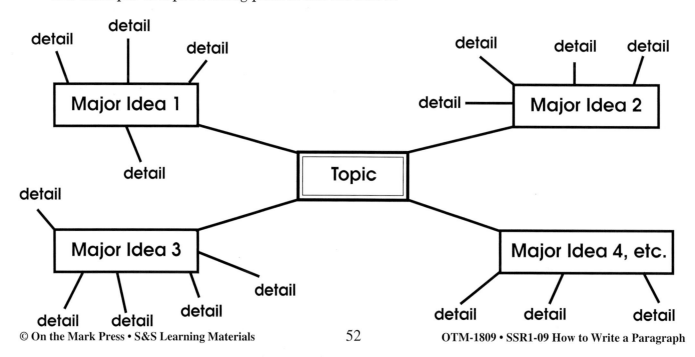

USING THE WRITING PROCESS (Continued)

WRITING THE FIRST DRAFT

Most beginning writers need to work on content and organization; style will come later; and mechanics can be helped by proofreading, editing or using one of many computer programs. The steps in the Prewriting stage will help to provide adequate content for the essay. What follows is a simple pattern which should help the student to organize the paragraph. The pattern can be changed to meet the requirements of the specific writing task.

Various patterns can be developed for beginning each form of writing. The requirements of a particular piece of writing will determine the pattern to be used. It is important that the writer catch the interest of the reader at the beginning of the piece; it is also important in an exposition or a description to provide some kind of overview in the topic sentence as a guide for the reader.

1. Begin with a sentence which catches the reader's interest. In a narrative this may mean starting in the middle of the action. In a description or exposition, the opening may be a quotation or an interesting idea related to the topic. The idea of the opening sentence may be developed or explained in several sentences which follow it.

2. In a story develop the paragraph as necessary; be sure to include necessary background information in the first few sentences. In an exposition or description, state the overall topic in a single sentence.

3. Provide all the details of the plot (in a narrative) or the explanations, examples, descriptions in other forms of writing.

4. Conclude an exposition or description by restating the topic in a new way. When writing a narrative, end the paragraph in a way which is satisfying for the reader. Avoid the **I woke up** ending.

USING THE WRITING PROCESS (Continued)

EDITING AND REVISING

Editing and revising are not merely proof-reading. Rather they comprise a very important step in the writing process at which stage the student will do a thorough evaluation of his or her writing and will receive feedback from peers or parents. Students need to be taught **how** to edit; they should not simply be expected to know how to do it. Unless students are taught how to edit, peer edits will consist of comments like "Good work" or "Check spelling"--and these comments are of little practical use in improving a piece of writing.

Students should begin to learn how to edit in the later grades of elementary school, and continue to learn how to edit through secondary school. The editing directions which follow are designed for elementary school and early secondary school students. More complete editing suggestions will be found in *How to Write and Essay*, SSR1-08.

Students often have more difficulty editing their own work than editing someone else's work. It is, therefore, good practice for students to peer edit, not only to help the other student to improve, but also to learn how to improve their own writing.

Editing works best if the student keeps in mind the four categories--**Content, Organization, Style and Mechanics.** Each of these categories will be examined briefly in the following pages. There are various activities, particularly in the Mechanics section, which will help students learn how to edit their own and their classmates' work.

Peer editing should be looked at in two ways: A good peer edit not only helps the writer, but also the editor. Students perhaps learn more from editing someone else's writing than from editing their own. Perhaps this knowledge gained from editing other students' work will eventually carry over to their own writing.

USING THE WRITING PROCESS (Continued)

EDITING AND REVISING

EDITING FOR CONTENT

The teacher should always make perfectly clear to students what the expectations of an assignment are. These expectations will normally highlight what is expected in terms of content. Teachers should provide students with a clear editing sheet for any particular assignment, if the teacher expects students to edit their own or each other's work for content.

Bearing that in mind, the teacher may use what follows as part of the editing sheet for a paragraph.

Editing and Exposition or a Description:

1. Have all the relevant questions been answered in the pieces of writing. Relevant questions may include:

   · Who?
   · What?
   · Where?
   · When?
   · Why?
   · How?

2. Has sufficient detail been provided by the writer? If so, provide examples of good detail. If not, where in the paragraph could more detail be added? Do you have any suggestions that may add detail to the paragraph?

3. Are there parts of the paragraph which you do not understand? Is this lack of understanding caused by the way the paragraph is written or by the omission of important information? If important information is missing where could it be added?

4. Is the paragraph interesting? Does it have an interesting opening and an interesting conclusion? Are the middle sentences interesting? If so, which ones? If not, which ones?

USING THE WRITING PROCESS (Continued)

EDITING AND REVISING (Continued)

EDITING FOR CONTENT

Editing a Narrative:

1. Opening:
   - Does the story open in an interesting way?
   - Are there better ways to begin the story? If yes, what are they?

2. Plot:
   - Does the plot move at an appropriate pace?
   - Does it reach a climax?
   - Is there a satisfying conclusion to the plot?

3. Setting:
   - Has the writer provided enough detail about time and place so that the reader gets a "feel" for the setting?

4. Characterization:
   - Do the characters exhibit real emotions and behavior?
   - Are the characters only names without personality or appearance? If yes, where might the writer describe or develop the characters in the story? What character traits might be appropriate?

5. Theme:
   - What is the story about?
   - Does the message come through clearly? If yes, where does this occur? If no, what could the writer do to make a clearer message?

Sections 3 and 4 on *Editing an Exposition or a Description* (page 55) could also be used here.

For more information on the terms used here, please see *How to Write a Composition*, SSR1-10.

USING THE WRITING PROCESS (Continued)

EDITING AND REVISING (Continued)

EDITING FOR ORGANIZATION

A Check List of Questions to Ask:

1. Does the opening sentence catch the reader's interest? Why or why not?

2. Is there a clear topic sentence for the paragraph?

   • If so, which sentence is it?

3. Does the paragraph possess unity; that is, does each paragraph discuss only one main idea?

4. Is the paragraph coherent; that is, does the paragraph flow smoothly with a logical arrangement or order?

5. Are transitions used to provide coherence?

6. Is there a concluding sentence?

   • If so, does it do an effective job in finishing the paragraph?

   • In an exposition or description, does the concluding sentence sum up the topic of the paragraph?

   • In a narrative, does the concluding sentence provide a satisfying ending to the story?

USING THE WRITING PROCESS (Continued)

EDITING AND REVISING (Continued)

EDITING FOR STYLE

Style is the most sophisticated of the four components of the writing process and is developed through writing programs to and including the university level. Students at elementary school can begin their study of style through writing and editing.

We often use the word *style* in reference to fashion, as in *style of clothes*. A person with style is said to possess a knowledge of the latest trends, a certain flair. In writing, **style** refers to the way the writer uses **language** to create specific **effects** or to reach certain **goals**.

Thus, style is the use of words and the arrangement of words to form sentences.

For more information on style, please refer to *How to Write an essay*, SSR1-08.

Questions to Ask about Style:

1. Does the writer use effective and precise nouns and verbs in the composition? Which are particularly good examples? Which nouns and verbs are particularly vague or colorless?

2. Are adjectives and adverbs used effectively? Are they overused? Might some of them be replaced with more colorful nouns and verbs?

3. Does the writer use imagery? Is the imagery effective? Does the writer use old and worn out similes and metaphors? Does the writer create new and original similes and metaphors?

4. Does the writer use the sounds of words effectively? Do the sounds of words present an appropriate tone?

USING THE WRITING PROCESS (Continued)

EDITING AND REVISING (Continued)

EDITING FOR MECHANICS

Mechanics in writing refers to some of the most basic components of language programs in the elementary school--spelling, grammar, punctuation, and sentence structure.

Not all students have the same problems with mechanics. Some are good spellers; others are not. Some have persistent problems with certain aspects of grammar; others have a good grammar sense. Some students speak and write in sentences; others always speak and write in incomplete or run-on sentences. While the school curriculum provides basic instruction in all these aspects of mechanics, some students will need constant reminders of the areas they can improve.

There are many aids available for students who have weaknesses in mechanics. Spell-Check on computers is a valuable aid, but requires a knowledgeable proof-reader. Grammar checks on computers are more difficult to use, since much of the way we write depends on personal preference.

Although there are many individual differences, generally students seem to have difficulty with only a few areas of mechanics. Those which students often need to focus on are:

- · common errors in spellings
- · the use of the apostrophe
- · the use of a consistent verb tense
- · agreement of pronouns and antecedents
- · the use of the semicolon (usually covered in secondary school).

Only the first two (common errors in spelling and use of the apostrophe) are dealt with in this resource. Teachers and students needing information on the other topics should consult *How to Write an Essay*, SSR1-08.

USING THE WRITING PROCESS (Continued)

EDITING AND REVISING (Continued)

EDITING FOR MECHANICS (Continued)

Common Errors in Spelling:

Many students have no difficulty in spelling and are able to see their errors clearly when they edit their writing. Others have a great deal of difficulty. There are, however, words which students consistently misspell and students need to be aware of these. A writer can easily improve spelling if he or she is on the lookout for specific words which cause problems. Following is a list of words that appear incorrectly spelled in many students' writing:

- receive: The "*i before e*" rule has too many exceptions to be considered a rule. Generally, "*ei*" will follow the letter "*c*", and students need to bear this in mind when writing words like **receive, deceive, conceive, ceiling**.

- achieve: There are many words which follow the rule such as: **achieve, friend, piece, chief** and **relieve**.

- separate: Note that the letter "*a*" follows the "*p*".

- definite: Note "ite", not "*ate*".

- their, they're, there: Their is possessive, meaning "belonging to them". They're is the contraction for "there are". There means "in that place".

- occurred, occurring, referred, referring, preferred preferring: These words double the letter "*r*" before adding "*ed*" or "*ing*". Note also **occurrence** doubles the "*r*", but **reference** and **preference** do not.

- dependent, independent: These adjectives are spelled "*ent*". Dependent with an "*a*" is a noun often seen on income tax forms to mean "someone who is dependent".

- words beginning with a prefix such as "un", "re", or "mis": Simply add the prefix to the word, as in **unnecessary, recommend** or **misspell**.

Activity on Spelling:

Create your own spelling collage, using a piece of bristol board. Make a list of words you misspell. When a word appears on the list three times, put it on the bristol board collage.

USING THE WRITING PROCESS (continued)

EDITING AND REVISING (Continued)

EDITING FOR MECHANICS (Continued)

The Use of the Apostrophe:

Some students have difficulty using the apostrophe correctly. The rules which follow are very simple. Many writers try to complicate these rules by making exceptions to them, but these rules can cover every major example of the apostrophe.

Uses of the Apostrophe:

- Possession in Nouns
- Contractions

The apostrophe is used to show **possession** or **ownership**. Originally possession was shown in Anglo-Saxon by the addition of the letters "*es*" to a noun. The "*e*" was later omitted and the apostrophe was used in its place.

The apostrophe is also used to show the omission of letters in **contractions**. Contractions are two words shortened into one word by omitting letters. Some common contractions are *didn't* (the letter "*o*" is omitted), *who's* (meaning *who is*), *they're* (meaning *they are*).

Using the Apostrophe to Form Possession:

Singular nouns form possession by adding *'s* to the noun. Follow this rule and you will always be correct, even if the noun ends in *s*. Some examples:

- Boy= singular noun   Boy's= belong to the boy;
- Mr. Smith = singular noun   Mr. Smith's = belongs to Mr. Smith
- Brutus = singular noun   Brutus's = belonging to Brutus
- Dickens = singular nouns   Dickens's = belonging to Dickens

Plural nouns ending in *s* form possession by adding *'* to the noun. Example:

- Boys= plural noun   boy's= belonging to the boys

Plural nouns not ending in *s* form possession by adding *'s* to the noun. Some examples:

- Children = plural noun   children's = belonging to the children
- Data = plural noun   data's = belonging to the data
- Women = plural noun   women's = belonging to the women.

USING THE WRITING PROCESS (Continued)

EDITING AND REVISING (Continued)

EDITING FOR MECHANICS (Continued)

The Use of the Apostrophe (Continued):

Writers who follow the rules on page 61 will **never be wrong** in forming possession. There are writers and grammarians who complicate these rules by saying that if the singular noun ending in *"s"* is pronounced *"es"* then on adds *'s;* if the word is not pronounced *es* then add only the apostrophe; *Jesus'* sake (meaning for the sake of Jesus) would then be pronounced *Jesus sake*, but *Jesus's sake* would be pronounced *Jesuses sake.* This kind of usage is often found in hymns or prayers using poetry, but for the most practical purpose it unnecessarily complicates a simple rule of the English language (and really there are not very many simple rules that apply, are there? So why complicate it?)

Using the Apostrophe with Pronouns:

The apostrophe is **never used with personal pronouns to form possession;** it is used only to form **contractions.** Here are some examples:

- *who's* = who is; the possessive is *whose*
- *their's* does not exist; the possessive is *theirs*
- *our's* similarly does not exist; the possessive is *ours*

Indefinite pronouns, however, **use the apostrophe to form possession.** Indefinite pronouns are words like *one, everyone, anyone*, etc. Here are some examples:

- everyone's job
- one's own work

These simple rules will govern the use of the apostrophe. Many students have difficulty with the concept because they either confuse the meaning of the term possession or they are overwhelmed by the number of seeming exceptions. If the teacher stresses that there are no exceptions, then the task becomes easier for students to learn.

USING THE WRITING PROCESS (Continued)

EDITING AND REVISING (Continued)

EDITING FOR MECHANICS (Continued)

The Use of the apostrophe (Continued):

Activity on the Use of the Apostrophe:

1. Form the possessive of each of the following words:

    a) the boy
    c) Mr. Jones
    e) My mother
    g) Tomatoes
    i) Brothers

    b) Judy
    d) Americans
    f) Japan
    h) Michael Jordan
    j) Tennessee.

2. Four words in the following sentence contain incorrect apostrophes. Four other words are missing required apostrophes. In groups of two or three, decide which are the four incorrect words and which four words need apostrophes. Be prepared to support your answers.

> In his work Dickens often writes about evil society. He knows about debtors prison because his father spent some time in a prison. He knows also about the evils' of the workhouse, where people who are very poor have to live in order to eat. Oliver Twist is a character who's life begins in a workhouse, but Oliver is adopted by a rich family. However, Dickens does not believe that life is easy. Oliver is kidnapped by Fagin and his boys who are pickpockets'. The boys steal from people but they arent sorry for it. The pickpockets' job is really to support Fagins lifestyle by providing him with articles he may sell. An acquaintance of Fagin named Nancy tells Olivers new parents where they can find him, Nancy's boyfriend, Bill Sykes, kills' her. Finally, Fagin and Bill Sykes are punished for their crimes. Dickens novel, <u>Oliver Twist</u>, clearly shows problems in society.

USING THE WRITING PROCESS (Continued)

WRITING THE FINAL COPY

If a student has followed all the steps in this resource, writing the final copy of the paragraph will be simple, because all the work has been done. A student who wrote the first draft on a word-processor has been able to make revisions quite simply. Now all that needs to be done is to put the program through spell-check and format it to fit the pages.

What follows is a check-list for the final copy of the paragraph:

- Be sure that the paragraph is double-spaced and that adequate margins have been left on all sides.

- Use the accepted format for footnotes and bibliography if these are required. See *How to Write an Essay*, SSR1-08, for additional information.

- Add a title page. Some teachers like students to put their writing into duotangs because these add a touch of formality to the assignment; other teachers do not like duotangs because they add more bulk. Since the teacher has to carry the work home or to another room to begin the arduous job of marking, he or she may resent the bulk caused by duotangs. The student should check with the teacher before submitting the paragraph.

- Proofread the paragraph carefully. Even a good spell-check program will not be able to catch typographical errors.